THE TREASURY OF
VOCAL MUSIC

BOOK **4** THREE-PART
SONGS SSA

KU-367-370

Edited by
WILLIAM L. REED D.MUS. *and* ERIC SMITH D.MUS.

STIRLING COUNTY LIBRARY

STIRLING
DISTRICT
LIBRARY

BLANDFORD PRESS · LONDON

878679

784.3
REE

First published in 1969
© 1969 by Blandford Press Ltd,
167 High Holborn,
London W.C.1

SBN 7137 0053 X

Printed in Great Britain by
Lowe & Brydone (Printers) Ltd., London

784.3
REE

THE TREASURY OF VOCAL MUSIC

BOOK **4** THREE-PART
SONGS SSA

PREFACE

THE present series of books has been conceived with the classroom in mind and in the hope that it will offer to students a change from what has tended to become a somewhat narrow and faded repertoire.

We have included several lesser known works of the great composers as well as some new compositions, and those standard items from the classics which are retained will, we hope, have their usefulness enhanced by the new and eminently singable translations specially made for this edition by John Morrison. We have not sought to provide books for specific classes or grades of proficiency because we realise that the latent talent in every class will respond to the demands of something exacting and, at the same time, appreciate something which can be accomplished satisfactorily with comparative ease.

We offer these books in the hope that they will fill a gap in the repertoire by providing some additional worthwhile material to sing, and that they will extend the ever widening horizons of music in schools, further education establishments and, indeed, all places where music is made.

William L. Reed

Eric Smith

London, January 1969

CONTENTS

I. LULLABY, MY SWEET LITTLE BABY

WILLIAM BYRD
Adapted and arranged by
EDMUND H. FELLOWES

Copyright, 1925, by Stainer & Bell Ltd.

2. LIFT THINE EYES
(from 'ELIJAH')

FELIX MENDELSSOHN

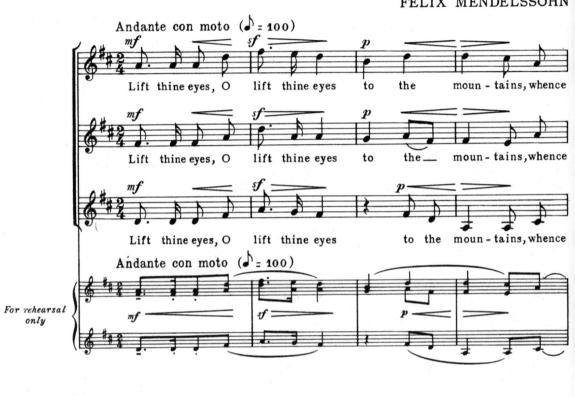

For rehearsal only

3. WEEP YOU NO MORE, SAD FOUNTAINS

(from John Dowland's 'THIRD AND LAST BOOK OF SONGS', 1603)

DAVID SYDNEY MORGAN

© Copyright, 1969, David Sydney Morgan

4. LADY, THOSE EYES

THOMAS MORLEY
Edited by EDMUND H. FELLOWES
Revised by THURSTON DART

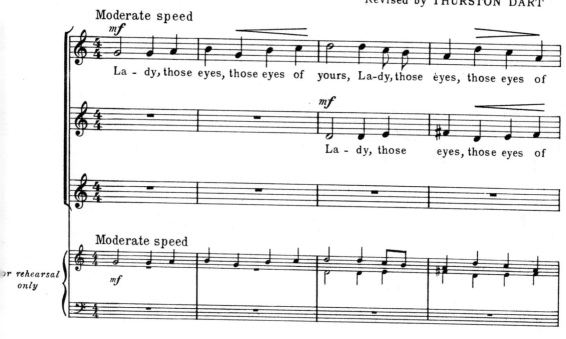

opyright, 1913, by Stainer & Bell Ltd.

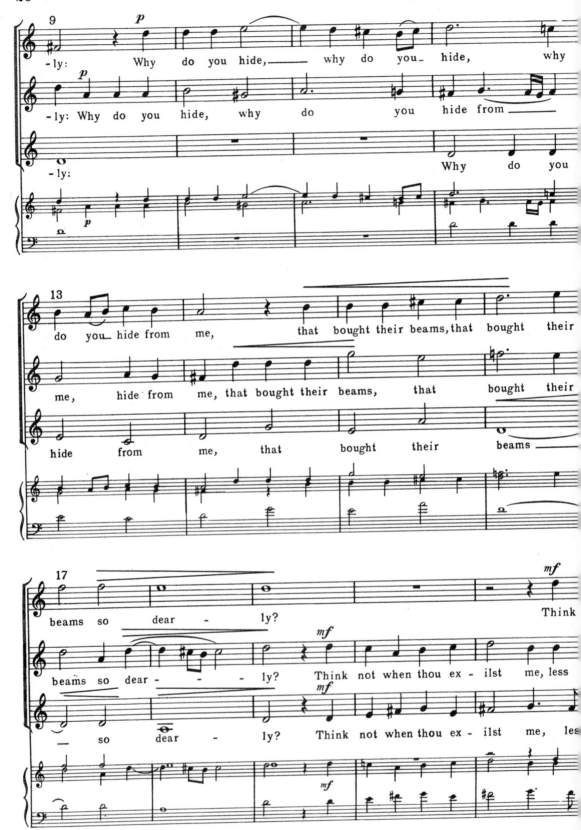

5. DEATH OF A NIGHTINGALE
AUF DEN TOD EINER NACHTIGALL
(CANON)

After the poem by LUDWIG HÖLTY
Translated by JOHN MORRISON

WOLFGANG AMADEUS MOZART, K.2?

She is gone, is gone, is gone, She, our
Sie, sie ist da - hin, da - hin, sie, die

She is gone, is gone, is gone,
Sie, sie ist da - hin, da - hin,

She is gone, is
Sie, sie ist da

For rehearsal only

sing-er of __ May, __ Whose songs en - chant - - -ed,
Sän-ge-rin, die Mai - - -en - lie - der tön - - -te.

She, our sing-er of __ May, __ Whose songs en -
sie, die Sän-ge-rin, die Mai - - -en - lie - der

gone, is gone, She, our sing-er of __ May,
-hin, da - hin, sie, die Sän-ge-rin, die Mai -

Songs that o - ver wood and grove __ des - cant -
Sie, die durch ihr Lied den Hain __ ver - schön -

-chant - ed, Songs that o - ver wood and grove __
tön - te. Sie, die durch ihr Lied den Hain

Whose songs en - chant - ed, Songs that o - ver
- en - lie - der tön - te. Sie, die durch ihr

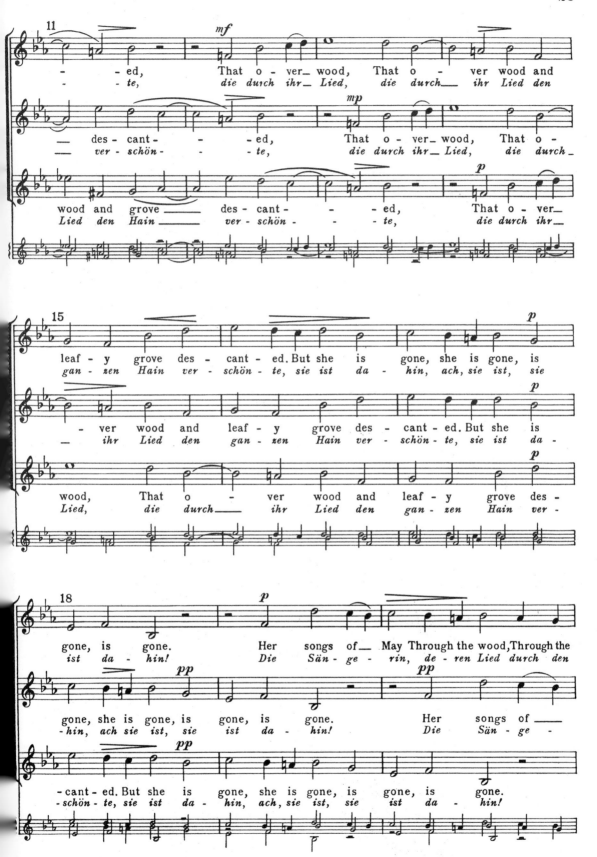

6. SPRING, THE SWEET SPRING

THOMAS NASH

GEORGE OLDROYD

For rehearsal only

Copyright, 1923, by J. Curwen & Sons Ltd.

sting,   cold__ doth not sting,   The pretty birds do_ sing, _____

Cold doth not sting,   not sting,   The pretty birds do_ sing, _____

Cold doth not sting,   not sting, not   sting,_____ The pretty birds do_ sing,

17   *rit.*

_____ The   pretty birds do_ sing,_____

_____ The   pretty birds do_ sing,_____

_____ The   pret - ty birds,_ the pretty birds_ do sing,_
                                                        rit.

22 *pp* a tempo   *mp*

Cuc - koo,   cuc - koo,   Jug jug,   jug jug jug jug,   pu-we,   pu - we,   To-wit - ta
pp   *mp*

Cuc - koo,   cuc - koo,   Jug jug,   jug jug jug jug,   pu-we,   pu - we,   To-wit - ta
pp   *mp*

Cuc - koo,   cuc - koo,   Jug jug,   jug jug jug jug,   pu-we,   pu - we,   To-wit - ta

a tempo

pp   *mp*

Lyrics under the staves:

56
Jug jug, jug jug jug jug, pu-we, pu-we, To-wit-ta
Jug jug, jug jug jug jug, pu-we, pu-we, To-wit-ta
Jug jug, jug jug jug jug, pu-we, pu-we, To-wit-ta

59
woo, to-wit-ta woo,___ to-wit-ta woo.___ The
woo, to-wit-ta woo.___ The
woo, to-wit-ta woo.___ The

65 L'istesso tempo
fields breathe sweet,___ The dais-ies kiss our feet,___
fields breathe sweet,___ The dais-ies kiss our feet,___
fields breathe sweet,___ The dais-ies kiss our feet,

Young lov-ers meet, Old wives a-sunning sit,_____ In

Young lov-ers meet, Old wives a-sunning sit,_____ In

Young lov-ers meet, Old wives a-sunning sit,_____ In

ev-'ry street these tunes_____ Our

ev-'ry street these tunes_____ Our

ev - 'ry street, in ev-'ry street these tunes_____ Our

ears_____ do_ greet,_____

ears_____ do_ greet,_____

ears do greet, our ears_____ do greet,_____

7. A CRADLE CAROL

JOHN MORRISON

ENID RICHARDSON

Very smoothly and with expression

1. Peace-ful and ho - ly is the night,
2. Laid in a man - ger for a bed,

For rehearsal only

Shep-herds a - lone their flocks at - tend. What is that
Cat - tle stand round to keep Him warm. Whose is that

8. COME SHEPHERD SWAINS

JOHN WILBYE
Edited by EDMUND H. FELLOWES
Revised by THURSTON DART

Copyright,1914, by Stainer & Bell Ltd.

9. FROM THE GREEN HEART
OF THE WATERS

NYMPH'S SONG from 'ULYSSES'

STEPHEN PHILLIPS SAMUEL COLERIDGE-TAYLOR

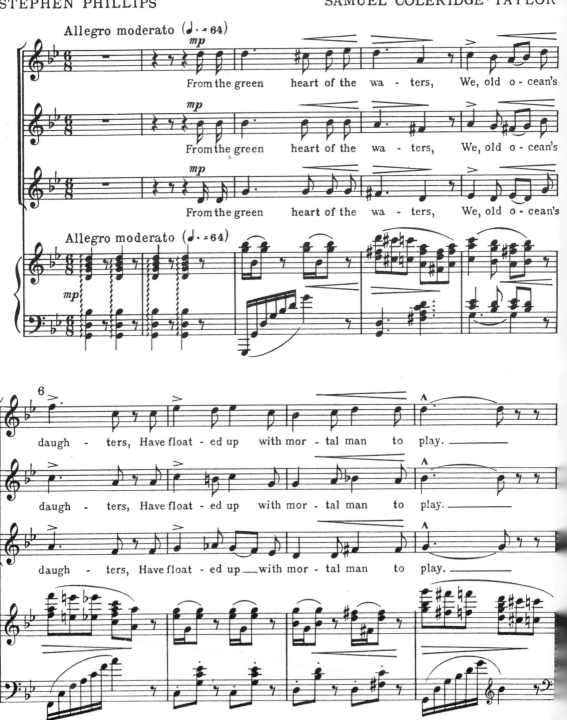

10. HYMN TO THE WATERS
(from 'CHORAL HYMNS FROM THE RIG VEDA')

GUSTAV HOLST

te. (4-3) denotes that each bar is divided into one of four beats followed by one of three: (3-4) denotes that the three
ats come before the four.

Opyright, 1912, by Stainer & Bell Ltd.

sky   Who dug the path for you to

(A♮)

(4-3)

(4-3)

run.

(4-3)(B♮)

dim.

pp Tutti

Flow - ing from the fir - ma-ment   Forth to the o - cean,

pp

Flow - ing from the fir - ma-ment   Forth to the o - cean,

pp

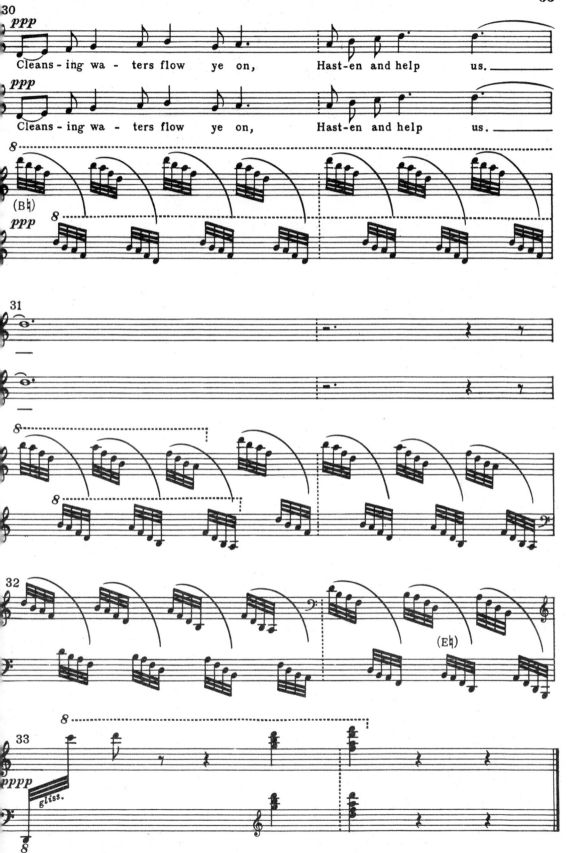

II. O YOUNG MEN JOYFULLY PRAISE THE LORD

LAUDATE PUERI

Translated by
JOHN MORRISON

FELIX MENDELSSOHN, Op. 39, No.
Edited by ERIC SMITH

*The second section is omitted

12. A HYMN TO BEAUTY

IERNE ORMSBY *

GEORGE OLDROYD

* The words are used by kind permission of the authoress.

Copyright in U.S.A. and all countries, 1947, by the Oxford University Press, London.

His bless-ing fell as dew___ on grass-y blades, ___

His bless-ing fell as dew on grass-y blades, ___

His bless-ing fell as dew on grass-y blades, ___

And hailed the soar - - - ing lark. ___

And hailed the soar - - - ing lark. ___

And hailed the soar - - - ing lark. ___

I guessed his

I guessed his

I guessed his

beau-ty by the daff - o-dils, And ev'ry wood-land scent, _____

beau-ty by the daff - o-dils, And ev'ry wood-land scent, _____

beau-ty by the daff - o-dils, And ev'ry wood-land scent, _____

_____ I felt Him in _ the wind a-bout_the hills _____ An

_____ I felt Him in the wind_ a-bout_the hills An

_____ I felt Him in the wind_a-bout_the hills An

13. COLD WINTER'S NIGHT

Words and Music by
PENELOPE THWAITES

Cold win-ter's night, hard frost was on the ground, ___

Bright shone a ___ star to ___ where a King might be found. ___

Lord of both king and shep-herd, Lord of ___ rich and poor Of ___

© Copyright **1969** Penelope Thwaites

17 ev - 'ry__ na - tion, Lord __ of all. __

C D Gm A7 D7 Gm

20 All Lord of both king and shep - herd, Lord of __ rich and poor, Of __

Lord of both king and shep - herd, Lord of rich and poor, Of

Gm C Gm C6 Gm

24 ev - 'ry __ na - tion, Lord __ of all. __

ev - 'ry na - tion, Lord of all. __

C D Gm A7 D7 Gm

O - ver the hills came men of wealth and learn - ing,

O - ver the hills came men of wealth and learn - ing,

Shep - herds, their hearts with awe and won-der burn - ing,

Shep - herds, their hearts with awe and won-der burn - ing,

Knelt where they found Him sleep-ing in an ox - en stall, A

Knelt where they found Him sleep-ing in an ox - en stall, A

Child in a man - ger, Lord ___ of all. ___

Child in a man - ger, Lord of all. ___

Ah ___

Ah ___

(Hum) ___

(Hum) ___

ev - 'ry na - tion, shin - ing through ev - 'ry wall, Till __

ev - 'ry na - tion, shin - ing through ev - 'ry wall, Till

all men ac-know-ledge Him Lord __ of all! __ Ah __

all men ac-know-ledge Him Lord of all! __ Ah __

14. SPINNING SONG
(from 'THE FLYING DUTCHMAN')

Translated by
JOHN MORRISON

RICHARD WAGNER
arr. ERIC SMITH

15. MUSIC, WHEN SOFT VOICES DIE

ERCY BYSSHE SHELLEY

CHARLES WOOD

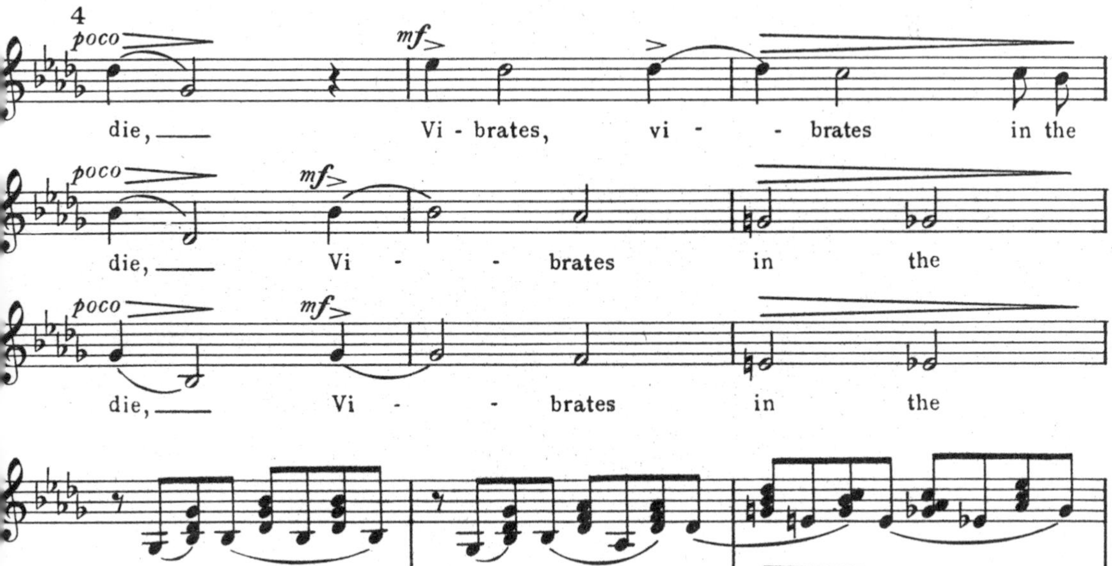

By permission of Ascherberg, Hopwood & Crew, Ltd.

And so thy thoughts, when thou art gone,

And so thy thoughts, when thou art gone, Love

And so thy thoughts, when thou art gone, Love

Love it - self ___ shall slum - ber, shall slum - ber

___ it - self shall slum - ber, shall slum - ber

___ it - self shall slum - ber, shall slum - ber

on.

on.

on.

STIRLING COUNTY LIBRARY